TopGear

AWESOME
ADVENTURES:

VIETNAM

Stuff they
did on TV.
In a book.

TOP GEAR

BBC Children's Books
Published by the Penguin Group
Penguin Books Ltd, 80 Strand,
London WC2R 0RL, England
Penguin Group (Australia) Ltd, 250
Camberwell Road, Camberwell, Victoria
3124, Australia (a division of Pearson
Australia Group Pty Ltd)
Canada, India, New Zealand, South Africa

Published by BBC Children's Books, 2010
Text and design © Children's Character
Books, 2010

10 9 8 7 6 5 4 3 2 1

Adapted by Sam Philip from the
BBC *Top Gear* Vietnam Special
television script
Internal design by Dan Newman

ISBN: 978-1-40590-699-9

Printed in Slovakia.

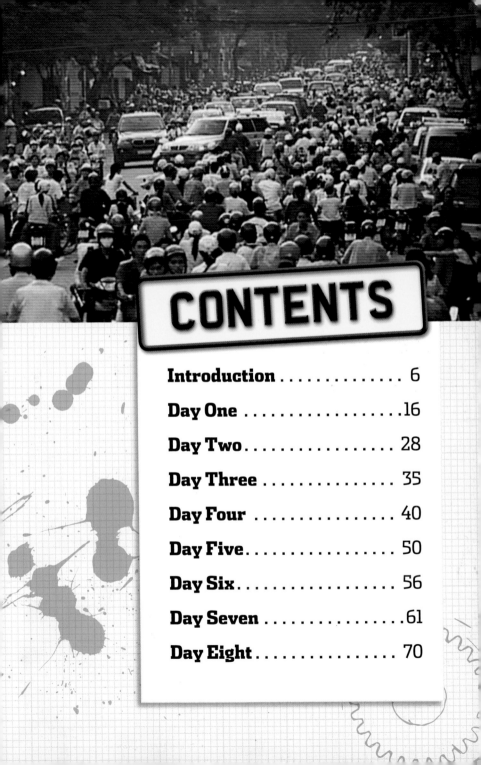

CONTENTS

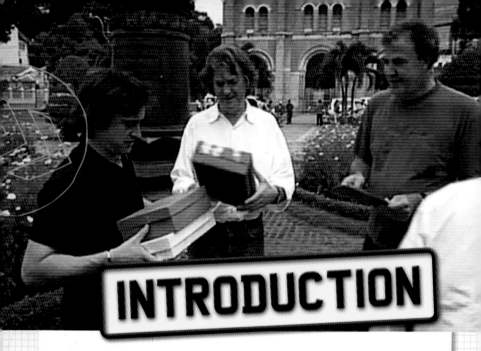

INTRODUCTION

Jeremy opened the envelope. "Since you can buy Rolexes here for a fiver, and lunch for 50p, you're standing in the world's biggest pound shop," he read. "You should therefore have no trouble at all buying some wheels for 15 million dong."

"Fifteen million?" asked James in disbelief. The dong was the main currency in Vietnam. Fifteen million sounded like a lot of dong.

The three boys were standing in the main square in the centre of Saigon, the largest city in Vietnam, and a strange man in a white jacket had just handed them an envelope and three heavy shoeboxes. But what did the shoeboxes contain?

VIETNAM'S BIGGEST CITY

Saigon is the largest city in Vietnam, and is home to over seven million people – about the same number as London. The city and its surrounding area is also known as Ho Chi Minh City, named after Ho Chi Minh, the president of Vietnam from 1945 to 1969.

CHINA
VIETNAM
LAOS
CAMBODIA

Look at **that!** Fifteen million dong!

I love the smell of **money** in the morning.

Smells like... **wheels.**

"Are these full of money?" said James, opening one. He was right: each shoebox was full to the brim with foreign banknotes. Fifteen million dong looked like a lot of money. This seemed odd: usually the boys were given a very small amount of money to buy a car, so why had the strange man in the white jacket been so generous?

James soon discovered the problem. The boys had split up to buy their cars, and James headed straight for a garage selling new Fiats. He spotted a nice black Fiat 500, a car that would cost about £10,000 in the UK.

REALLY BIG BANK NOTES

The dong has been the official currency of Vietnam since 1978. One-tenth of a dong is known as a hao, but this is worth such a tiny amount of money that it is no longer used. The biggest bank note issued is 500,000 dong – but this is only worth about £18!

One thousand US dollars? That was about seven hundred pounds in Britain. That wasn't very much money to buy a car. James decided to head to a second-hand car dealer on a quiet back street to see if he could find anything cheaper.

Jeremy had found the same problem as James. Out on the busy streets of Saigon, he was becoming desperate.

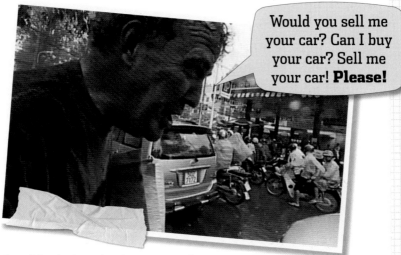

Would you sell me your car? Can I buy your car? Sell me your car! **Please!**

Richard had already given up and found a street-side café for lunch, when he was joined by Jeremy and James.

"Pull up a chair," said Richard, knowing full well that the furniture was far too small for Jeremy – who is taller than many full-grown giraffes – to fit on. He smiled as he watched Jeremy and James trying to wedge themselves under the small table.

"I said to you all along that you two are the freaks," Richard smiled. "This place is perfectly scaled." All of the furniture in Vietnam was slightly shorter than back in Britain, which suited Richard just fine.

AVERAGE HEIGHT

Vietnamese people are among the shortest in the world. The average height of a Vietnamese man is 162 centimetres tall – almost 10cm shorter than Richard Hammond! Here's how the Top Gear boys line up against the tallest – and shortest – countries in the world:

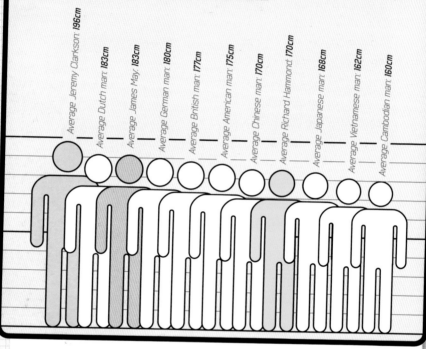

Average Jeremy Clarkson: 196cm
Average Dutch man: 183cm
Average James May: 183cm
Average German man: 180cm
Average British man: 177cm
Average American man: 175cm
Average Chinese man: 170cm
Average Richard Hammond: 170cm
Average Japanese man: 168cm
Average Vietnamese man: 162cm
Average Cambodian man: 160cm

"I'll tell you what the problem is," said Jeremy, bringing the conversation back to the big car problem. "Cars only came to Vietnam a few years ago. Four or five years ago. They've got a two hundred per cent import tax on them. They haven't had time, in the four or five years since they've been here, to get cheap."

"So there are no bangers?" asked Richard, already knowing the answer.

"It's expensive and we're actually quite poor," said James.

It was starting to look as if the three boys had flown a very long way for nothing. Even if they put all of their money together, they still couldn't afford to buy a car. But as they looked out over the bustling streets of Saigon, packed with motorbikes and scooters each carrying two, three, sometimes even four people, James and Richard had an idea.

"Look around us, what do we see everywhere?" Richard asked, pointing at a row of motorbikes parked neatly next to their table. Jeremy understood immediately what he meant.

MILLIONS OF MOTORBIKES

There are over 20 million motorbikes in Vietnam, compared to about one million in the whole of the UK. In Saigon, there are three million motorbikes and scooters, one for every two people in the city.

"No," said Jeremy firmly. Unlike James and Richard, who both owned motorbikes back in the UK, Jeremy hated them and had never learned to ride. "You know I can't do that."

"Well, what else is there?" asked James.

Jeremy was silent.

"It's transport with an engine," agreed Richard. "It's the only choice we have."

"Come on," said James, getting up from the small table with difficulty.

"No," said Jeremy again. But he knew he had no choice...

THE VIETNAM WAR

Before we go any further, we ought to mention the war, because it's important to the rest of the story. The Vietnam War was one of the world's bloodiest conflicts since the Second World War, fought between Southern Vietnam and the American army on one side, and Northern Vietnam and its communist allies on the other.

It raged from 1959 to 1975, and resulted in the death of over six million people, including 1.2 million North Vietnamese troops, over 300,000 soldiers on the South Vietnamese side, and nearly 60,000 US troops. The war ended with the North Vietnam troops capturing Saigon and toppling the Southern regime, and the Americans fled the country.

Even 35 years later, the war is burned in the memory of the Vietnamese, many of who believe the Americans should not have been involved in a war so far away from their own country.

An hour later, the three boys met up at the American War Museum with their second-hand motorcycles. Richard was first to introduce his bike to the others.

"I bought this – it's a **Minsk**," he said cheerily. "Russian, 125cc. It's rugged, simple, easy to repair. It is built specifically to be used in countries where there are no roads. It will be, for whatever they throw at us, perfect."

Next, it was James's turn.

"I've gone completely native and I've bought this, an ancient **Honda 50 Super Cub**, the greatest motorcycle in history," he gushed. "Over 60 million of these have been built and it is a greater

liberator of the people than... well, that American tank, for example."

Finally Jeremy introduced his bike.

"I've bought this," he said, pointing disdainfully to his bike, which was lying helplessly on its side. "Which is, erm... a **motorcycle**."

"Well," said James, butting in. "Technically, this is a scooter."

"It is," agreed Richard. "You really don't know anything about bikes, do you?"

"Nothing," said Jeremy cheerily.

"It is very pretty," said Richard, consolingly. "But it's going to be useless, because whatever the challenge is, tiny wheels and looking good are not going to help you."

"Why are tiny wheels wrong?" asked Jeremy.

VIETNAM WAR FILMS
The Vietnam War has inspired hundreds of films, including: Good Morning Vietnam and Forrest Gump

"Because the holes in the road are big and the little wheels go further into them," said James.

Jeremy looked depressed. "How many cylinders has it got?" he asked, referring to his bike's engine.

"One," said Richard.

"One?" repeated Jeremy, in disbelief. He was used to proper cars, with eight, ten, or twelve cylinders. One was not very many cylinders at all.

At that moment, the man in the white jacket mysteriously reappeared, brandishing another envelope. James opened it.

"You will now attempt to achieve in eight days what the Americans failed to achieve in 10 years," he read. "Get from the south of Vietnam to the north. You will ride from here in Saigon to Ha Long City near the Chinese border, which is one thousand miles away."

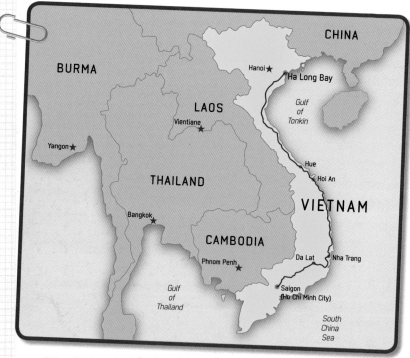

"Wow!" shouted Richard happily.

"That is the best challenge we've ever had!" agreed James.

Jeremy was impassive. "I can't do that," he said. "Guys, I can't do that. I can't ride a bike. This is stupid."

"I can't believe you're being a misery guts!" said James.

"It's a thousand miles in the rainy season in a country with not-very-good roads," complained Jeremy. "And I can't ride a bike."

Jeremy had a point. Vietnamese roads are incredibly dangerous,

TopGear

especially if you don't know how to ride a motorbike. Four times more people die on Vietnamese roads than in Britain, and Jeremy was certain he would add to that statistic over the next eight days. The first thing to do, he decided, was to get a helmet. This proved surprisingly difficult, as Vietnamese helmets are all made for people with smaller heads than Jeremy.

"The reason I don't ride a motorcycle is because I have a large brain," reasoned Jeremy later, as the three boys tried on helmets in a Saigon bike shop.

"No," countered Richard, who had already found a helmet that fit his head perfectly. "You have a very big head."

"The reason why crash helmets are small," argued Jeremy, "is because people who wear them haven't got a brain, otherwise they'd have a car."

But for all his reluctance, Jeremy knew he would have to get a helmet from somewhere. So, as night fell on Saigon, he and James found a back street metal shop that they hoped would create some helmets for them...

DAY ONE

The next morning, the boys met up to set out on their epic journey. But James and Jeremy's helmets hadn't turned out exactly as they hoped. Jeremy seemed to be wearing a bucket, while James had a large wok strapped to his head.

Because he couldn't turn his head very far in his bucket hat, Jeremy had also added some mirrors to his scooter. LOTS of mirrors.

MOD STYLE
Jeremy's scooter now looks like those ridden by Mods, a group defined by their smart clothes and cool taste in music. Just like Jeremy.

CHUG-CHUG-CHHHHÚÚÚG!

And with that, James and Richard zoomed off into the distance, leaving Jeremy to try and start his bike. He didn't know how to start his bike.

Stupid thing!

Many minutes of cursing later, a friendly passer-by stopped to help Jeremy. With some difficulty, she helped him onto the bike and got the motor started. He eased off the clutch and, finally, he was up and running.

Clunk! After just a couple of seconds, the bike coughed and spluttered and ground to a halt. Jeremy had stalled it.

"It's been a **hour** and I've done **three feet**," he said gloomily. With yet more help, he restarted the bike and hesitantly weaved out into the traffic.

"He's going to **die**," said the friendly passer-by, as she watched him wobble slowly off into the distance.

While Jeremy struggled with his bike, James and Richard were having a great time weaving out of the city through the mad traffic. James had converted his wok-helmet to a more streamlined colander arrangement, and was

TopGear

marvelling at the busy roads of downtown Saigon.

"Whoa!" shouted Richard over the noise. "I've been riding bikes for twenty-five years and I've never done anything like this! It's amazing! I'm glad we couldn't afford cars!"

"I think you just improvise!" bellowed James back, squeezing past a scooter carrying what looked like a dozen people.

"Is this your favourite place in the whole world?" yelled Richard, a happy smile on his face.

"Yeah!" whooped James.

Far behind them, Jeremy had ditched his bucket-helmet and found some more sensible headwear... but he wasn't enjoying himself.

This is terrifying... it's just bikes absolutely **everywhere**... oh, get into gear!

Gearbox has a mind of its own, there's **no** suspension, it's just wobbling all the time.

You're going the **wrong** way!

Out of Saigon and into the countryside, Jeremy eventually caught up with Richard and James. They all pulled over to a roadside petrol station to take a look at Jeremy's wobbly bike.

"Thanks for waiting!" snapped Jeremy.

"I thought you were just behind us," pretended Richard.

"You **knew** I wasn't just behind you," sulked Jeremy. He pointed to the front wheel of his bike to explain why he had been so slow. "That nut is as tight as it can go, and it's loose!"

A mechanic at the petrol station diagnosed a broken driveshaft, which spelt seriously bad news on a Vespa scooter.

"We're going to have to change the whole engine," said Jeremy gloomily. But at least this time his mates wouldn't leave him behind... would they? He looked up to see James and Richard disappearing off into the distance on their bikes...

James and Richard rode north, enjoying the peace and quiet of a Clarkson-free journey. With Jeremy far behind, waiting for some helpful locals to fit his bike with a new engine, they stopped for lunch in a small café. Richard looked down the menu in horror...

I think this thing here is some sort of squid... with some weird paste.

I don't like squid.

I don't like clams.

OK, you can have crab with –

I don't like crab.

Razor clams?

Several miles back down the road, a team of a dozen mechanics had fixed Jeremy's bike, and he was back on the road.

The wheel is no longer wobbling, it's got a new engine and a new gearbox... and it feels **exactly** the same! Crummy, rubbish, **useless.**

Richard and James, still far ahead, had finished their lunch and were making smooth progress through the lush, green countryside.

These bikes are quite a common sight all over the world...

> These are the wheels of Asia. Over **60 million** of these bikes have been sold. Combine the Volkswagen Beetle, Model T Ford, all the versions of the Toyota Corolla and the Mini... and you **still** haven't got as many as you have of these.

The hot, muggy day rolled on, and the boys pounded relentlessly on to Da Lat, with Richard and James out in front, and Jeremy and his wobbly broken scooter far behind them. As evening fell and the air cooled, Richard and James had reached the steep, tropical hills that climbed to their destination for the night.

AS POWERFUL AS A HORSE?

Horsepower (or bhp) is used to measure the power of cars and motorbikes. Most modern family cars produce around 100bhp, and the most powerful production car in the world – the Bugatti Veyron – produces 1,000bhp! Here's how the boys' bikes line up against a few other powerful things.

Horse	1bhp
James's Honda	4bhp
Jeremy's Vespa	8bhp
Richard's Minsk	10bhp
Aprilia RSV4 superbike	180bhp
Bugatti Veyron	

James's Honda, with its tiny four horsepower engine, was struggling to climb the roads. As the road became steeper, the bike slowed to crawling pace, no matter how hard he revved the engine.

Just admit it, you should have bought a more powerful bike.

No, I'm not admitting it yet. I'm still going!

I'm going ahead to check it out, to see if it gets steeper.

I'm coming to a dignified failure. She's going, she's going, she's **gone.** That's it, I've run out of power...

But at least James hadn't stuck fifteen mirrors in front of his own headlamp. Jeremy had. As night fell, he realised this had not been such a sensible idea . . .

1,000bhp

I'm riding along with the headlight illuminating nothing but my **own face!**

Ahead, James had walked his motorbike the last few miles to Da Lat. He arrived, panting and sweaty, at the agreed restaurant, to find Richard relaxing with a cold drink. There was still no sign of Jeremy.

"Where do you reckon he is?" asked Richard.

"Don't know," replied James, in a weary tone that suggested he simply didn't care.

I am the most **miserable** human being alive! **Where** is this restaurant? **Where is it?**

Many hours later, James and Richard were lying comfily on the restaurant benches, having a drink and gazing up at the ceiling. Jeremy staggered through the door, looking dirty, tired and thoroughly angry. His first day on a motorbike hadn't gone well.

The three boys sat down to order food. Richard looked hesitant as he gazed over the menu. He was suspicious of foreign food, but Jeremy ordered a set menu and watched Richard's discomfort.

"You haven't eaten anything since you got here, have you?" asked Jeremy.

"I have!" protested Richard. "You just... haven't seen me."

"He had some cornflakes," piped up James.

"I was trying them just in case they were different," lied Richard. "I like to try local cultures and flavours, and they may have been different cornflakes..."

ANYONE FOR DINNER?

Vietnamese food is very different to English food. It is mainly based around rice dishes, and uses ingredients like fish sauce, soy sauce and coriander. Many people think it is one of the world's most delicious cuisines.

But Vietnam is also famous for some very strange dishes, including:

Duck embryos
Silk worms
Sparrows
Fermented fish
Deer
Dog
And beating snake heart!
Now, who's feeling hungry?

He was interrupted by the arrival of the 'set menu'. The waiter was holding a six-foot-long snake that was still very much alive.

I don't **like** snake.

It's going to be delicious. Could I have it medium rare?

Medium rare snake?

How would you have it cooked? **Well done**, I suppose?

TopGear

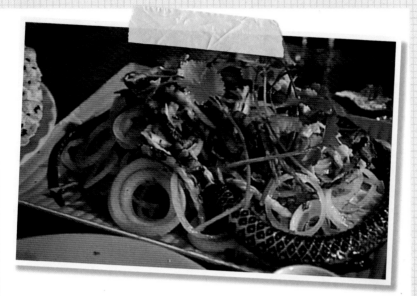

The snake was skilfully butchered before their very eyes, and Jeremy and James settled down to a delicious meal of snake salad, snake soup and, most gruesomely, still-beating snake heart. Richard, of course, ate nothing at all.

As Richard left to get an early, hungry night, Jeremy and James decided to play a harmless prank on him...

Did you do this?

Yes.

We just wanted to make sure it was strong enough.

We tested it by putting it under the wheels of a lorry... and look what happened!

DAY TWO

The next morning, the sun rose peacefully over the Vietnamese hills. On the street outside their hotel, Richard strode angrily over to Jeremy and Richard, holding his flattened helmet in his hand. It definitely hadn't been flattened when he'd left it on his bike the previous night.

"It's **ruined!**" shouted Richard.

"Don't worry," said Jeremy, calmly. "We've bought you another one."

He proudly brandished a bright pink helmet and presented it ceremonially to Richard.

"Don't take this the wrong way," reasoned James. "Colours assume different significance in different cultures –"

"**Stop talking!**" snapped Richard, who had certainly taken it the wrong way.

"Seriously," continued James. "In Britain we think of pink as a feminine colour, but here it's the colour of warriors!"

"Stop!" shouted Richard, storming off to start the day's 130-mile journey with his bright pink helmet.

"He's not very happy with us, is he?" muttered James to Jeremy.

"He's not," replied Jeremy.

Barely had James and Jeremy jumped on their bikes and caught up with Richard when it started to rain. Not a gentle drizzle, but a true monsoon, a mighty storm that flooded the road and soaked them to the bone. The locals, used to such weather, simply wore giant raincoats to keep themselves dry, but the boys hadn't come so well prepared...

IT'S RAINING … RAIN!

If you thought Britain was wet, try visiting Vietnam! Average rainfall in Vietnam can be as much as three metres per year, about three times the usual rainfall in the UK.

Name an upside to this. Name **one** upside!

Well, you're not hot any more.

Why has my life gone so wrong?

It's good for you.

It is **NOT**.

Richard's bike was the first to conk out in the rain, but soon after James and Jeremy passed him, it was the turn of James' Honda to splutter to a halt.

"How can it have run out of petrol?" shivered James, standing by his lifeless bike, as the rain turned the narrow Vietnamese road into a mud-red river. "That rain makes a really **annoying** noise on my colander-helmet. And it comes through..."

Further down the road, Richard had made some emergency repairs to his Minsk, and sped past James before catching up with Jeremy, who had briefly taken the lead. Picking their way over broken, drenched roads – and avoiding huge trucks doing the very same thing in the opposite

direction – the two boys pulled over at a countryside filling station to replace Richard's broken clutch cable. As the weather slowly turned from Very Wet to A Bit Less Wet, they were joined by James.

"May, there's **bad news**," said Jeremy, grimly.

"What?" asked James.

"The producers have got fed up with us just replacing parts willy-nilly on our bikes –" started Jeremy.

"You two, you mean?" interrupted James. He hadn't needed any parts yet, but Jeremy had already replaced his entire engine, while Richard's bike was sporting a shiny new clutch.

"They say," continued Jeremy, "that if our bikes go wrong again and we can't keep them going using tools, they've provided backup transport."

TopGear

"**Excellent!**" said James, imagining a shiny new bike or, even better, a car. But, as Jeremy pulled the covers off the 'backup transport' that the producers had left for them, his excitement was short-lived.

It was certainly a shiny new bike, but it was painted entirely in the colours of the American flag. It had a pair of American flags hanging from the back and, somehow, was playing *Born In The USA* by Bruce Springsteen. It wasn't clear how it was playing *Born In The USA* – it didn't seem to have a stereo – but it was.

A crowd of villagers started to head towards the three boys and their new bike. They didn't look happy.

"This is about as **inappropriate** a bike as it's humanly possible to conceive," said Jeremy slowly, as the locals nearby stared at the American Bike with undisguised hatred. There was now a very, very good reason to avoid replacing any more parts on their bikes.

Mysteriously, all three bikes suddenly began working perfectly.

> **I am Francis Rossi!** This is staggeringly good! We are in the clouds!

The boys made good progress as the sun burned the rainclouds away and the mountain roads became even more spectacular. Even Jeremy, who hated motorbikes very nearly as much as he hated caravans, started enjoying himself.

THE WRONG ROSSI?

Francis Rossi is the lead singer and guitarist from dad-rock band Status Quo. Surely Jeremy meant Valentino Rossi, the Italian motorbike racer who's won the MotoGP world championship six times?

But all the stops earlier in the day had cost them time, and as night and heavy clouds fell over the mountains, the boys still had many miles to cover before they reached their stop for the night in Nha Trang. For the first time since leaving Saigon, though, they were together in convoy, and as the last of the sunlight finally disappeared, a dramatic lightning storm lit up the hills around them.

> Oh no! **No!** My light! My light!

Jeremy's front headlight fizzled out and he careered through the darkness, with only the flashes of lightning to find his way. He considered stopping for help and a replacement light, but remembered the American Bike and instead decided to simply strap a torch to his front

mudguard and hope for the best. The conditions were treacherous, as rain hammered down and trucks swept past at 50mph, within inches of the struggling bikes.

Deep into the night, the three bikes wobbled into Nha Trang, a city spread along one of the most beautiful sandy bays in the world. But between the pouring rain, the inky darkness and the mad traffic, the boys weren't admiring the views.

> Got to be careful on the downhill bits!

> This is where it gets **bad.**

> There's no other word, it's absolutely **suicidal.**

James took the lead, ploughing across junctions and squeezing through tiny gaps between cars, lorries and scooters with Jeremy and Richard following in convoy. When they reached the hotel, all three boys were exhausted from another day of torrential rain, terrifying traffic and temperamental bikes.

As James and Richard headed to a restaurant to find dinner, Jeremy wandered off into the town centre to do a bit of late-night shopping. A while later, he returned armed with a big present for Richard and a knowing smile...

There you go. A nice present.

That's for me? Why?

Because I thought it would look good in your new house. Have you seen the detailing on it?

Richard stared at the huge galleon for a while, unable to understand why Jeremy had given him such a generous gift. Then the realisation struck him.

"I see what you've done," he said, smiling resignedly.

Jeremy grinned. "If you had a car," he said, "you'd pop it on the back seat or in the boot..."

He didn't need to say any more. Richard thought about the inconvenience of lugging a five-foot-long model ship on the back of his scooter for another 800 miles, and groaned to himself.

DAY THREE

D ay three, and the boys were back on the road, ploughing towards Ha Long through a hot, humid morning. The roads were flatter than the previous day, but as dangerous as ever: packed with potholes and speeding buses and thousands of weaving scooters.

Richard had somehow managed to lash his galleon across the back of his bike, and was wobbling along with a grimace on his face. Vietnam, Jeremy thought as he peeled his shirt away from his skin, did not have the finest climate for motorcycling: it was either sticky, hot and damp, pouring with rain... or all four.

More than two hundred miles of riding on dusty, muddy roads had taken its toll on the boys' clothes. They looked awful, plastered in dirt and sweat and squashed insects. After a couple of hours of riding, they decided to stop at the coastal town of Hoi An to buy some new clothes.

As luck would have it, Hoi An just so happened to be famous for its skilled tailors, renowned for creating suits at a fraction of the price of the tailors back in Europe. Buoyed by their good fortune, Jeremy, James and Richard dropped into the first suit makers they could find to check out the local wares...

This is cashmere?

Yes.

And how much is this suit?

One hundred and thirty five US dollars.

Jeremy did some quick mental arithmetic.

"A cashmere suit... for seventy pounds?" he asked, in astonishment. Back in London, a handmade suit would cost ten times that amount.

"How long will it take?" Richard asked.

"It will take one day to produce your clothes," answered the saleswoman.

"We can have any style... and any material," mused Richard, realising that this would also be a good excuse to spend a day off his motorbike. "Right lads, I'll need some time on my own!"

He strode off to get measured for his suit. Jeremy and James quickly decided that they, too, rather liked the idea of a new handmade suit, and wandered off to look through the baffling array of fabrics.

A few minutes later, Jeremy tiptoed over to Richard, holding a tiny child-sized dummy dressed in a full suit.

Your suit's **ready**. Here it is.

Thank you. That's... very nice.

After much choosing of material and stretching of tape measures around their legs, arms and just about every other body part, the three boys decided on the exact specification of their suits.

As their new wardrobes wouldn't be ready until the next morning, Richard and James suggested that the three of them take a nice trip down to Hoi An's beautiful beach... with their bikes.

As James and Richard revved down to the water's edge, Jeremy snuck off to find a posh hotel. While he sipped a cocktail and soaked his feet in the outdoor swimming pool, down by the sea James and Richard were competing to see who could get their bikes nearest to the waves, drenching themselves and their bikes as they blasted through the shallows.

Why are we doing this? I've fallen off! **I've fallen off!**

Desperate to beat James in the getting-your-bike-closest-to-the-waves competition, Richard had accidentally got his Minsk completely soaked through.

I am now officially the world's **most comfortable** man. Ahhh...

Worried by the looming presence of The American Bike, he carefully propped it up to dry off, and fell into conversation with an elderly local man. Though he didn't speak a word of English, it was clear he wanted to tell Richard a story. He knelt down in the sand and started to draw with his finger, a picture of a plane, and a few numbers and letters.

You were here... fighting against the US... in 1968. B-52s... deaf. This beach is yours. **I'll go...**

Richard left the beach, quickly and quietly, suddenly aware of what a devastating impact the war in Vietnam still had on its people.

It also made him realise exactly how bad it would be to have to ride The American Bike for the rest of the journey, Right on cue, Richard discovered that his recently-soaked Minsk wouldn't start. As dark fell and Jeremy and James set off into Hoi An for some dinner, Richard enlisted some local help to get his Minsk working again. The American Bike hovered nearby, blaring out Bruce Springsteen.

"If Richard turns up on Bruce Springsteen," shouted James to Jeremy as they biked into the centre of Hoi An, "I'll feel quite sorry for him... but I'll still laugh."

THE PLANE, NOT THE BAND

The **B-52** is an American military aircraft most famous for its bombing raids on Vietnam during the war in the 1960s. Thirty American B-52s were lost during the Vietnam war.

Their conversation was cut short as they rounded a corner to be greeted by an extraordinary sight: thousands and thousands of rainbow-like candles, floating on the surface of the calm, cool water in the heart of Hoi An.

Wow!

It's very pretty, I have to say.

Very pretty, and Hammond has **missed it**. This is like the duck racing they do on British rivers, only much more beautiful...

Back at the hotel, Richard worked frantically on his still-dead Minsk, the sound of Bruce Springsteen ringing in his ears...

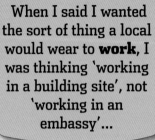

When I said I wanted the sort of thing a local would wear to **work**, I was thinking 'working in a building site', not 'working in an embassy'...

DAY FOUR

Another Vietnamese day dawned bright, and another huge road trip beckoned, this time on to the ancient Vietnamese capital of Hue. The three boys dropped into the tailors, dressed in their newly-created suits, and headed out onto the coastal highway.

To his great relief, Richard had managed to dry out his Minsk, which was now running sweetly. In his new orange suit – matched with a snappy yellow shirt – and with his model ship still lashed to the back of the bike, he was getting a few odd looks from the locals. Not that his two fellow riders looked any less strange: James sported a loose, dark blue suit with a Chinese dragon

embroidered on the front, while Jeremy was wearing a shiny, bright blue suit with a flowery shirt underneath.

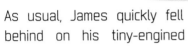

Love your work, is that a smoking jacket?

As usual, James quickly fell behind on his tiny-engined Honda. Knowing how depressing it was to bring up the rear, Jeremy and Richard generously stopped at a roadside shop to buy James a nice present.

Unfortunately, the shop seemed to only sell large, heavy statues, which would be very inconvenient to carry on the back of an ancient Honda Cub. But, kindly, they decided to treat James anyhow...

We decided to buy you a **present**. We know that you like the ballet...

... and we thought about it long and hard...

I need some straps.

Richard and Jeremy christened James's new statue 'Darcey Bussell', after the famous English ballerina of the same name. Once Darcey had been strapped to the back of the Honda, the three boys set off once again, with James riding even more carefully than usual to avoid any possible damage to his new present.

But Richard wasn't taking the same care. Just a few miles after setting off, he squeezed his Minsk too close to a line of bins and caught the side of the galleon against them. With a cracking, splintering sound, the masts of the boat split free of the deck and wrapped themselves into a tangled, broken heap around the back of Richard's bike.

"Your masts have come off!" shouted Jeremy, drawing alongside. "They're all down!"

"I can fix that!" shouted Richard back. "You'll never notice!"

It didn't look very fixable. And, a few minutes later, things went from bad to worse for Richard. As the three bikes skimmed through a toll booth in the motorway – where cars had to stop and pay, but motorbikes were allowed to pass through for free – Richard, forgetting the extra width of his ship, slammed the end of the model galleon into the toll booth sign with a loud 'thunk'.

Further down the road, Jeremy's Vespa put-put-putted to a halt. Again. Panicked by the thought of having to ride The American Bike for the rest of the journey, he quickly enlisted some locals to help him fix his scooter. By the time James – and Darcey – caught up with Jeremy, the bike was running smoothly again.

"You're not going to believe how they mended it," grinned Jeremy.

"With a hammer?" guessed James. "With a screwdriver?"

"No," said Jeremy. "With a plastic bag. They filled it with weeds

and then wedged it among all of the electrics, so they can't... jiggle about."

He tapped the saddle of the revived Vespa, and then looked to the north, where a huge, dark green mountain hulked over the horizon.

"See that mountain up there, James?" he asked.

James glanced up at the mountain. "Yeah?" he replied.

"We're going up there," smiled Jeremy.

"Right," said James cheerfully. "I'll wait for you at the top..."

The huge mountain turned out to be many mountains: the Annamite mountains, to be exact. They were steep and they were green, but, more than that, they were home to an astonishing stretch of road.

You expect to find many things when you come to Vietnam, thought Jeremy as he flashed through a series of beautiful curves, high up above the clouds that hung over the sea: reminders of the war, stunning food, massive heat – but what you don't expect to find is a deserted ribbon of perfection, one of the best coast roads in the world.

Known by the locals as the Hai Van Pass, which translates as 'Ocean Clouds', the road clung to the sides of the mountains like a piece of spaghetti, with the sea far away to the right and sheer, tree-covered cliffs to the left. On this road, Jeremy finally discovered that he actually rather enjoyed riding a motorbike...

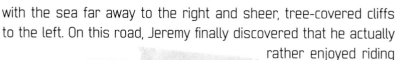

> I'm **liking** this. I'm going for an overtake. **Yeah!**

> This is **great!** At last I've got a playmate!

Far behind them, James's Cub wasn't enjoying the road quite so much...

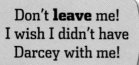

> Don't **leave** me! I wish I didn't have Darcey with me!

Richard and Jeremy had stretched out a big lead over James when, high in the mountains, Jeremy's Vespa puttered to a halt.

"You know we mended it with weeds?" Jeremy reminded Richard. "Well, the weed bag doesn't work."

Richard wasn't especially surprised. He couldn't remember many mechanics back in England fixing cars with bags of weeds. Still, he thought as he gazed at the amazing view that stretched out below, there were worse places to break down.

Jeremy was similarly transfixed by the vista. "Some of the stuff here," he marvelled, "makes all my hair stand on end. Look at that view!"

From far in the distance, the buzz of a tiny Honda motorbike was getting steadily louder. Jeremy and Richard turned to see James struggling towards them.

"It's not a majestic sight, is it?" laughed Richard, as James drew to a halt beside them.

"Have you got his present?" Richard asked James, gesturing towards Jeremy.

"I put it in the camera van," said James, smiling knowingly.

"Have you really got me a present?" asked Jeremy, seemingly truly touched.

"Yeah," grinned Richard. "We've both been amazed that you've come up this road on your first bike. You deserve a present. James?"

Solemnly, James presented Jeremy with an enormous painting of a Vietnamese village scene, measuring three foot from top to bottom. It would be even more inconvenient to transport all the way to Ha Long than Darcey or Richard's galleon.

After hammering his weedy Vespa back to life and tying his painting to the back, Jeremy set off in pursuit of Richard and James, who had generously set off ahead to check for hazards. He caught them up and the three boys swept down the Hai Van

That's very... **striking**, chaps.

I shall try to look after this, Hammond, a bit better than you're looking after the **galleon** I gave you.

Funnily enough, that's the word I used.

Down into second gear for the difficult hairpin! Oh **yes,** knee down!

He's actually **enjoying** himself!

Pass, whooping and cheering as they tackled the tight corners and absorbed the glorious scenery.

The fifty miles to Hue flew by in a blur of hairpins and magical views. When they reached the hotel, Richard set about mending his treasured galleon, while James and Jeremy decided to get revenge on him for breaking the boat, their present to him... by spray-painting his bike bright pink.

Within a few minutes, a crowd of locals had appeared to help decorate Richard's bike, despite James and Jeremy's best efforts to stop them.

Can they really not organise a junction better than **this?**

Did he not believe you? Funny that...

I know he's cross, but I told him a chef did it.

DAY FIVE

The next morning, under glorious sunshine once again, the boys hit the road to head north once more. But, for some reason, the atmosphere between them was a little tense. Richard, in particular, seemed a *tiny* bit angry about something.

Giving Richard a wide berth, the three boys made their way to a nearby government building, where they'd been told to report for their next challenge.

"I think your bike looks **good**," said Jeremy to Richard, as they parked up and took the envelope from the mysterious man in the white coat. "It matches your helmet now..."

"Yes, I spotted that," stated Richard. "Very good. Thank you."

"James, just read the challenge and cheer him up," said Jeremy. "It'll be 'the person with the pinkest bike wins', I bet you."

James opened the envelope and began to read.

"The person with the pinkest bike–" he began.

"There you go!" crowed Jeremy.

"It doesn't actually say that," admitted James. "It says, 'You are about to enter what was North Vietnam, so it's as well your papers are in order. You will therefore take a Vietnamese driving test'."

Jeremy laughed. "That will just be one of those jokes ones, won't it?"

"Forward and backwards, six feet," agreed James.

"Cheer up," Jeremy said to Richard. "This is going to be a **doddle**..."

Half an hour later, it was clear that the test was not going to be a doddle. The three boys were wedged into a tiny classroom with twenty other driving students, listening to an instructor lecture them in Vietnamese. Vietnamese was not one of *Top Gear*'s better languages. The oral test, thought James, was going to be tricky.

The instructor turned to Richard and barked a question at him in Vietnamese.

"Oh no," groaned Richard, rising to his feet. The instructor continued to berate him, and then paused, clearly expecting an answer.

> Always give way to the car from the right!

> You had a one in a hundred chance of being right there. But you were in the **wrong** language...

Richard's answer didn't impress the instructor, who next turned to Jeremy. Again, she barked a question in quick-fire Vietnamese. Jeremy gulped and stood up, taking a deep breath... and replied in a babble of perfect Vietnamese. The instructor smiled, nodded and moved onto the next student. Jeremy had, somehow, passed the oral part of the test.

"What did you just do? How did you know?" stuttered Richard as Jeremy sat down with a satisfied smile on his face. Richard had no idea that Jeremy could speak even a word of Vietnamese, and now here he was, reeling off answers to a driving test.

"Did you not bother learning Vietnamese before you came here?" asked Jeremy, innocently.

Next came the practical element of the test. A large figure of eight had been painted on the courtyard in front of the test facility. All the boys had to do, they were told, was drive around the figure of eight on their bikes, without their wheels touching the white lines. It sounded simple, especially for a trio of such experienced bikists as themselves.

"Hammond!" called an instructor through a microphone. Richard jumped on his bike and headed for the figure of eight.

Richard had successfully negotiated the test course, and next it was James' turn to be called to the test track.

"He'll love this," groaned Richard as James wheeled his bike to the start line. "It's all about precision, going slowly and being accurate..."

"He's gone the wrong way," interrupted Jeremy. James, unbelievably had somehow taken a wrong turning on the simplest circuit known to mankind.

"It's a good spectator sport though, isn't it?" laughed Richard, and James wobbled uneasily off the course.

Somehow, though, James made it around the course, and was rewarded with a shout of 'James May... **Pass!**' from the tester. Finally, it was up to Jeremy to maintain *Top Gear*'s perfect record in the practical test.

It didn't go well. Within seconds, Jeremy had wobbled out of control and over the white lines.

"What he's doing, rather predictably," groaned Hammond, as Jeremy tried to wrestle his Vespa back on course, "is going too fast."

Jeremy scooted towards the other two with a sheepish expression.

"You failed!" shouted James.

"I've only been riding a bike five days," protested Jeremy. However, he was permitted to have another try immediately. Jeremy did just that... and proceeded to fail spectacularly again.

"He's spent less time in the circle than he was out the circle!" moaned Richard in despair, watching Jeremy stall his bike.

"Jeremy Clarkson... FAIL!" came the shout from the tester. Again.

Jeremy decided that the problem was his Vespa, so he grabbed James's Cub and took yet another shot. Yet again, he weaved miles from the test route. Yet again came the shout from the tester:

This is just impossible on these wheels! They're too **small!**

Jeremy Clarkson... **FAIL!**

"Jeremy Clarkson... FAIL!"

"Is he the most ridiculous human being in the world... ever?" Richard mused aloud. James nodded.

Jeremy wheeled the Cub over to Richard and Jeremy. "We're going to have to get going," he said, grimly.

"But we haven't got a licence!" objected James.

"That's because you failed your theory," replied Jeremy.

"You haven't been granted a pass for your practical test," Richard pointed out. "It's pathetic!"

"But as a team..." started Jeremy.

"As a team," continued Richard, realising his point. "We've done both halves of the test. As a unit, we are licensed. We could have a *Top Gear* licence with all of our faces on it..."

"...if we stick together!" concluded Jeremy. It seemed like a good compromise, and besides, they were getting well behind schedule if they wanted to make it to Ha Long within their eight-day time limit.

He stood up and stepped away from the Cub to jump back onto his Vespa. Without Jeremy holding it up, James's Honda toppled to the floor with the sound of breaking marble. Jeremy turned round to see Darcey in several shattered pieces on the ground next to the Cub.

"I'm sorry, James!" winced Jeremy.

"You're not sorry," snapped James, picking up his bike. "Please shut up..."

CRASH!

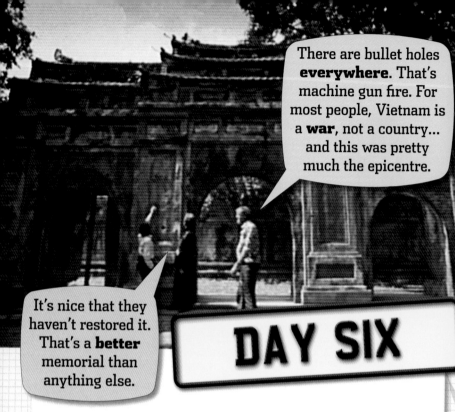

There are bullet holes **everywhere**. That's machine gun fire. For most people, Vietnam is a **war**, not a country... and this was pretty much the epicentre.

It's nice that they haven't restored it. That's a **better** memorial than anything else.

DAY SIX

Although they **were against** the clock, before they left Hue the boys decided to stop for a quick look around the Citadel, scene of one of the fiercest and most bloody battles in the Vietnam war.

DID YOU KNOW?
Eighty-five per cent of Vietnamese people are Buddhists. Thousands of Buddhist temples and pagodas are built around the country, some of which are many hundreds of years old.

Sobered by their experience, the boys set off north out of Hue. They were now on the fifth day of their monster road trip, with over four hundred miles left until they reached the finish line.

Progress was slow: the weather was getting hotter, the roads were getting busier and their bikes were straining and spluttering. James's Cub, which had been running sweetly earlier in

VIETNAM'S BIGGEST BATTLE

Hue's Citadel was the centre of the most violent battle of the Vietnam War. In January 1968, American and South Vietnamese forces clashed with the Viet Cong in a fight that lasted for nearly four weeks and saw the death of over 5,000 soldiers, and perhaps even more civilians. Around eighty per cent of the city was destroyed in the fighting.

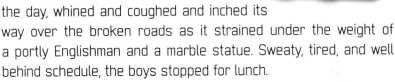

the day, whined and coughed and inched its way over the broken roads as it strained under the weight of a portly Englishman and a marble statue. Sweaty, tired, and well behind schedule, the boys stopped for lunch.

"Guys?" announced Jeremy grimly, as Richard eyed the menu warily. "**We can't make it**."

Richard nodded. "Thinking about it," he admitted, "that day spent playing on the beach and having a massage while we had our suits made... wasn't actually the–"

"**No**," interrupted Jeremy firmly. "But we can't just give in..."

Deep down, Richard and James knew Jeremy was right. The finish line was simply too far away: they had been riding for five days and had barely covered half the ground. With just three days left, no matter how hard they pushed their weary, rattly little bikes, they would never make it in time. Dejectedly, they agreed to catch the overnight train to Ha Long City.

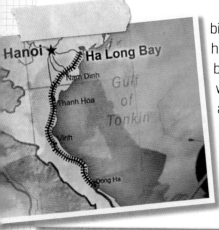

Later that day, the boys loaded their bikes onto the sleeper train. James, having already seen his beloved statue broken by Jeremy the previous day, was furious at Clarkson for ripping a six-inch hole in his painting – his present from Richard and James – with the spare wheel of his bike.

"Now look what you've done!" he exclaimed. "That was quite expensive!"

"You're not making me feel any better," replied Jeremy. "But let's not get bogged down in who did what to who..."

"No," said James. "Because you did all of it." He hauled his Honda into the train's freight carriage, grabbing the broken Darcey before heading off to the passenger carriage.

James had been put in charge of buying the tickets and, as the boys made their way to their reserved seats, it was clear he hadn't splashed out on any luxuries. The seats were in third class: crude wooden benches in a dingy, hot carriage.

"How long does this journey take?" asked Richard.

"Thirteen hours," replied Jeremy, surveying their sweaty surroundings.

"And how long have we done?" asked Richard.

"Er... four minutes," said Jeremy, his face sinking. It was going to be a long journey.

The boys decided to pass the time by mending each others' presents. Richard set about Jeremy's painting with a roll of gaffer tape and a few pots of paint, James tackled Richard's galleon with a pair of scissors, and Jeremy took a tube of glue to James' statue.

> Oh, it moves about more than I'd expected. It's OK, it'll give the painting some motion. It's good, it's good.

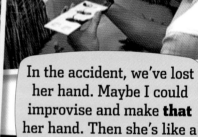

> In the accident, we've lost her hand. Maybe I could improvise and make **that** her hand. Then she's like a sort of mutant...

> It's like trying to unravel the mystery of the universe, made of **string**...

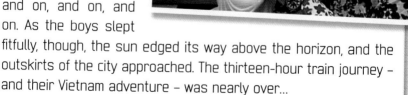

The night ticked on, and on, and on, and on. As the boys slept fitfully, though, the sun edged its way above the horizon, and the outskirts of the city approached. The thirteen-hour train journey – and their Vietnam adventure – was nearly over...

DAY SEVEN

With just a few minutes until the train was due to stop at their final destination in Ha Long City, Richard was surveying his handiwork with satisfaction. Jeremy wandered over to take a look at what Richard had done to his painting. He stared at the canvas for a while.

"What you've done..." began Jeremy, "is painted a Land Rover in the middle of a Vietnamese scene."

"Yeah..." admitted Richard, sleepily.

"You're in for a big surprise when you see what May's done to your galleon," smiled Jeremy.

Richard looked over at James, who was putting the final touches to his ship. It looked like a model version of a Viking longboat... created by a man with no arms.

> It's not brilliant, mate, if I'm honest. What are these?

> Chopsticks.

> What are they representing?

> Oars. It's a Chinese junk.

Their bickering was cut short as the train juddered to a halt. The boys rushed to the freight carriage to haul their bikes from the train, bashing and smashing their newly-renovated souvenirs as they went. In a bundle of string and paint and bits of statue, they wheeled their bikes out of the station and emerged blinking into the bright daylight of a north Vietnamese morning. With just a little cheating, they'd made it to the finishing line in Ha Long City, two days early.

"It hasn't been an elegant arrival," admitted Richard. "But here we are at the finishing point. It's very hot, isn't it?"

"Why isn't there a sea breeze?" asked Jeremy. Ha Long City was on the coast, but the hot, sticky air didn't feel very coastal. Something felt wrong. Richard looked up at the sign above the train station.

"How would you spell Ha Long?" he asked, slowly, squinting at the Vietnamese writing.

"H-A-L-O-N-G?" spelled Jeremy. He turned to look at the sign.

"It's two words," said Richard slowly, beginning to realise that something was indeed very wrong. "Because that means—"

"Hanoi!" realised Jeremy. They weren't in Ha Long City, they were in Hanoi, the second largest city in Vietnam, a city a long way away from their finishing line. His face sank.

"Where did you book the tickets to?" he asked, turning to look accusingly at James.

"There's nothing wrong with the tickets!" countered James, pulling them from the pocket of his suit. "Ha Long City!" he read. "Ha Long City! You chose the platform!"

"There was one platform, James!" shouted Jeremy. "There was one line."

"No, there was a line either side of the platform," argued James, "like there often is on a platform."

HANOI
Hanoi is Vietnam's capital and second -largest city. It is home to just over six million people, and celebrates its 1000th birthday in 2010!

As James and Jeremy bickered, Richard pulled out the map to assess the size of their error. It was, he estimated, 120 miles from Hanoi to Ha Long City, a long day of riding. Realising that they had to reach the finish line one way or another, the three boys reluctantly mounted their trusty bikes and headed out of Hanoi in what they hoped was the direction of Ha Long City.

The traffic was terrifying, even busier than it had been in the south of the country. After an hour of inching down gridlocked streets and dodging wild scooters, the boys stopped to get some breakfast.

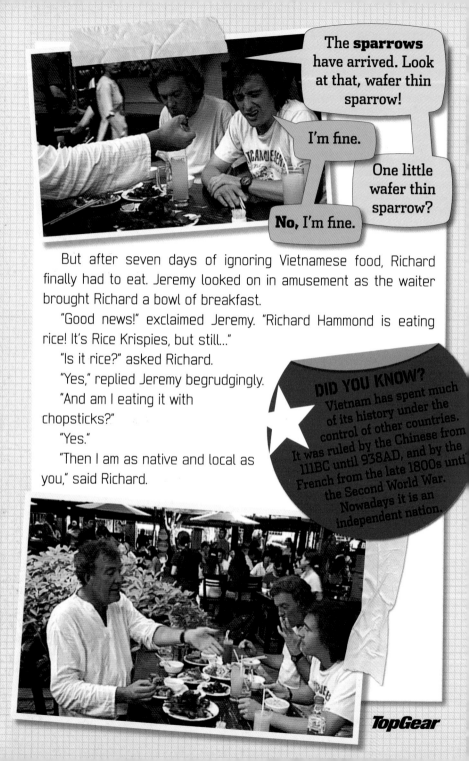

The **sparrows** have arrived. Look at that, wafer thin sparrow!

I'm fine.

One little wafer thin sparrow?

No, I'm fine.

But after seven days of ignoring Vietnamese food, Richard finally had to eat. Jeremy looked on in amusement as the waiter brought Richard a bowl of breakfast.

"Good news!" exclaimed Jeremy. "Richard Hammond is eating rice! It's Rice Krispies, but still..."

"Is it rice?" asked Richard.

"Yes," replied Jeremy begrudgingly.

"And am I eating it with chopsticks?"

"Yes."

"Then I am as native and local as you," said Richard.

DID YOU KNOW?
Vietnam has spent much of its history under the control of other countries. It was ruled by the Chinese from 111BC until 938AD, and by the French from the late 1800s until the Second World War. Nowadays it is an independent nation.

TopGear

Filled up on local and not-so-local food, the boys rode out of Hanoi for the final leg of their trip, in hunt of Ha Long City. It didn't start smoothly...

I've **no idea** where we are. No idea, not one sign post.

I'm pretty sure we've been past this park once already...

Finally, they found their way out of the city and deep into the countryside. This was good, but the complete lack of a main road was not.

"Ha Long and Hanoi are two big cities," said Richard, as the boys stopped to consult their woefully poor map. "I doubt they're connected by a three foot wide dusty path covered in hay."

"You know when we got to the 16th century?" joked Jeremy, as he surveyed their rural surroundings of rice fields and huts and piles of straw. "I think we turned left and we should have gone right. Now we're in the 13th century. We are completely lost."

"We're finally admitting that?" asked Richard.

"Even I will admit this is not the main road from Hanoi to Ha Long," conceded Jeremy, gazing over the peaceful rural scene around them. Cows grazed on the roadside as oxen shuffled past, dragging carts of hay. "But I like being lost here."

"Yeah," agreed Richard. "This is a nice place to be lost."

After a number of conversations with locals in which Jeremy seemed to have mysteriously lost his ability to speak Vietnamese, the boys were at last directed to the main road from Hanoi to Ha Long, a strip of proper tarmac.

With less than one hundred miles to go and the weather set fair, Jeremy realised they were finally going to make it. As they zipped along, at long last, a good piece of road, he reflected on his first experience on a bike.

I've always said to my children that if they buy a bike, I will **burn it**. And if they replace it with another one, I shall **burn** that too.

Now, however, if they buy a bike, I will **completely** understand. And **then** I'll burn it...

While Jeremy was making his speech, Hammond was going berserk with the elation of nearing the finish line. He leant back in the saddle and revved his Minsk for all it was worth, whooping out loud as he whipped by the traffic.

It was an ill-advised move: seconds later, his bike lost all power and puttered to a halt.

Ahhhhh! The speed!

He's just... a **prat**.

"No! No! I'm breaking down!" Richard shouted to Jeremy, who sped off into the distance. The American Bike was beckoning, but James pulled over to help Richard repair the Minsk. They'd made it nearly all the way to Ha Long without resorting to The American Bike, and he wasn't going to let Hammond down now.

Out in front, Jeremy's refusal to stop and help Richard came back to bite him. After overtaking a tractor, he caught a pothole with his front wheel and wobbled out of control at 40mph, tipping and crashing to the tarmac with a heavy thump. He shouted out in pain, but there was no one there to hear.

Back down the road, James and Richard had got the Minsk working, and were in high spirits as they zipped along to catch up with Jeremy, who they thought was far ahead. They winced as they reached the crash scene: a battered Vespa lying on its side, and an angry, bruised Jeremy being patched up by a local doctor.

It's my **first** bike crash, I'm a member of the club now. I **hate** biking, it's a **stupid** idea. My foot hurts, I've got cracked ribs, my elbow's ruined... **look** at my suit!

HA LONG CITY

Ha Long City is a small coastal city in the far north-east of Vietnam. It is one of the most popular tourist destinations in the country, and is famous for its beautiful bay and islands. Ha Long Bay has been protected by the United Nations as a World Heritage site since 1994.

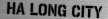

Ignoring their friend's rantings, James and Richard set off into the distance. Painfully, Jeremy hauled himself back onto his Vespa and caught up, shouting abuse at Hammond as he approached.

"Cheer up," smiled Richard. "We're nearly there!"

Richard was right: there was no time for squabbling. After nearly 700 miles on their bikes – and 250 miles on a train, but let's ignore that bit – they were nearly at the finish line. And, best of all, the weather was beautiful, an early evening of soft, golden sun.

"We've done it!" cheered Richard. "We've nursed these old, broken, tiny, weak bikes the length of Vietnam!"

"Ten miles to go!" chorused James, spotting a road sign.

The last few miles were a blur of honking, cheering and shouting. As the boys coasted to their final destination on the seashore in Ha Long and clambered sorely from their bikes, they were each smiling from ear to ear. It was a spectacular spot to end their trip: a sunset over a beautiful, calm bay.

As they shook hands and congratulated each other, the man in the white suit – where did he come from? – strode over and handed Jeremy an envelope. Why did they need an envelope? They'd finished, surely?

"It'll say congratulations. It'll say 'well done, you've reached the finish line'," reasoned Richard.

"It won't say that," said Jeremy.

"It is, it's going to say 'well done'."

"It doesn't. It says we haven't finished. It says, 'The actual finishing point is a bar in Ha Long Bay. As it's only accessible by water, it's probably a good idea to modify your bikes so they can float...'."

"No!" said Richard, in despair. All three of them had had enough: they were tired and sore and thoroughly sick of their bikes.

"But think," said Jeremy. "If it's possible to get a helmet made overnight, it must be possible to get your bike converted into a jet ski overnight!"

"Yeah, I'm sure they do it all the time," chipped in James.

"How hard can it be?" asked Jeremy.

"Don't say that!" snapped Richard.

As night fell, the three boys wearily set off in search of a local workshop to turn heir muddy, dusty bikes into vater-going powerboats...

DAY EIGHT

THE BAY OF DRAGONS

Ha Long is one of the true wonders of the world: a bay of nearly 2000 limestone islands that form a mysterious maze. In local legend, Ha Long Bay was created by a family of dragons, sent by the gods to defend the Vietnamese against Chinese invasion. The dragons spat out thousands of jewels into the bay, which turned into islands and formed a wall against the invaders.

The final morning dawned, and the boys stood on the beach, looking out over Ha Long Bay, one of the most spectacular views in the world. Hidden somewhere within the giant limestone maze was a floating bar. All they had to do was find it... and they had just the machines for the job.

James had attached his bike to a traditional fishing boat, using the engine to power the propeller.

It isn't a **motorbike** any more, is it?

Front wheels, **gone**. Engine, isn't where it's supposed to live...

There was **nothing** in the rules that said the engine had to stay in the same place...

They turned their attention to Richard's boat, which was a little more... spectacular.

> I have a rudder, then it's just a chain drive down to the prop, and I'm away.

> It's a **pedalo!**

> Yeah, this is just a pedalo with a few extra floats on it.

Jeremy's design was even more ingenious than Richard's motorswan. He had attempted to turn his Vespa into a Mississippi-style paddle steamer.

Jeremy's biggest problem, though, was not the weight of his boat, but that he couldn't kick-start his bike because of his broken ribs sustained in the accident the day before.

> My simple plan was very difficult, because the Vespa weighs **940,000 tonnes.** So I've needed four canoes full of foam...

"James?" he pleaded. "Could you start my engine for me? Neither of my legs are working."

"As you're injured, I'll reduce the price," replied James, generously. "Nine hundred thousand dong?"

Go away! Why are you doing this to me? It's **that way**, you blithering idiot!

After a quick bargaining session, all three bike-boats were up and running, and the boys set out across the bay in search of the bar. Very quickly, though, it all started to go wrong for James. First, he crashed into Jeremy's boat.

Why has it done that? Oh no!

Jeremy escaped, and James immediately became tangled in some fishing nets, just a few yards from shore. As Jeremy and Richard sped off towards the towering peaks of limestone, James began to slowly sink into the waist-deep water.

He hauled his boat back to shore and, with the help of a few fishermen, set about making his bike more seaworthy. Grabbing the spare pontoons left over from Hammond's pedalo, he watched as the fishermen tied the floats to his Honda, hoping it would fare a little better than his first effort.

As James dithered on the shore, Richard and Jeremy had made good distance out in the bay. But, inevitably, they had hit problems too. Jeremy's bike had stalled and, with his sore ribs, he needed Hammond to kick-start it back to life.

Richard nestled his motorswan into position and hopped across onto Jeremy's boat. He kick-started the Vespa and turned round to step back onto his swan. Which had drifted away...

Half an hour later, James was back on the water in his new, floatier bike-boat. He set off in pursuit of Richard and Jeremy, who had recovered Richard's boat but had become thoroughly lost. In search of the elusive bar in Ha Long's vast labyrinth of islands, they had resorted to hunting in the caves within the giant pointed rocks. Inevitably, they had got stuck. The boats had no reverse gears...

With a series of complex turning manoeuvres, Richard and Jeremy escaped the caves and continued their hunt for the bar. They had to reach the finish line before sundown, when their eight-day deadline expired. If the sun dropped below the horizon before they reached the bar, they would lose the challenge, and their journey would have been for nothing. Things didn't look good for James.

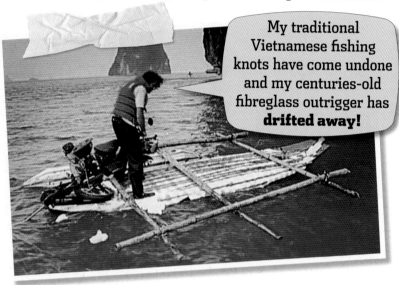

> My traditional Vietnamese fishing knots have come undone and my centuries-old fibreglass outrigger has **drifted away!**

Up ahead, Jeremy had left Hammond and his pedalo far behind, but there was still no sign of civilisation, no sign of the bar. Worse still, his Vespa seemed determined to have one final shot at killing him.

"Water has got into the electrical system and 60,000 volts is coursing through everything that's metal, including the frame of the bike!" he shouted, gingerly trying to steer his vessel without touching anything made of metal. He looked up.

Life! There's life! It's a bar! It's an umbrella! It's a **BAR!**

He turned round and bellowed at a speck in the distance, the opposite direction to the bar. "Hammond!" he yelled. "It's there! It's there!"

Hammond heard Jeremy's shouts, but could not do much with the information. His steering was broken, his swan paddling lamely round in loops. He watched as Jeremy inched agonisingly ever closer to the bar. How unfair, he thought, that the only non-biker among them was going to reach the finish line first.

As the sun dropped low, casting warm orange flickers across the water, Jeremy manoeuvred his bike-boat delicately to the edge of the bar, which floated, far away from the islands, in the centre of the bay.

All I can do is go round in circles...

Yes! And **that** is how we do that!

He had made it, reached the final destination. He cracked open a drink in satisfaction, and settled down in a deckchair to see if Richard and James could make it to the finish line before sundown.

Their progress was agonising. With James far behind, bumping into every one of Ha Long's 2000 islands, Richard edged towards the bar. Little by little, Hammond drifted towards Jeremy, spinning in circles as he tried to line up the swan for a final spurt at the bar.

Desperately, Richard splashed his hands in the water, edging the swan in the right direction. He gunned the throttle on his Minsk and, with a final ripple, he gently bumped into the pontoon and sprang onto the deck of the bar.

"Using nothing but currents and the wind, Richard Hammond's idiotic Minsk has made it." Cursed Jeremy.

As they watched the distant figure of James May drift slowly and helplessly towards them, Jeremy and Richard savoured their amazing location, a mountain paradise in the middle of the sea.

"I've just been finding out about this place," said Jeremy. "The people who live here are born here. They live here, they fish here and they die here."

"And they never go on dry land?" asked Richard.

"Never go on dry land," confirmed Jeremy.

"They just spend their whole life floating?"

"Just floating around..."

Floating, however, was becoming an issue for James. With minutes until sundown, he had drifted within fifty feet of the bar, but his boat had come apart and was rapidly sinking. Jeremy and Richard watched unhelpfully from the side as James lost his final shred of dignity, diving away from his collapsing craft and swimming the last few yards to the bar. As he grabbed the jetty and struggled to haul himself up, Richard and Jeremy were doubled over with laughter.

"This," giggled Richard, "is the **worst** arrival at a place ever made by anyone."

With a final struggle, James levered himself out of the water and collapsed onto the jetty. Triumphantly, he slammed down a heavy white object that he'd rescued from his sinking boat. It was the cracked, broken figure of Darcey, his beloved statue.

TopGear

The three boys sat on the deck of the bar, gazing at the setting sun, tired but happy. They'd made it, them and their little bikes. There had been breakdowns, accidents and squabbles, but through the rain, the draining humidity, the mad traffic and the tricky roads, their budget bikes had carried them a thousand miles. Er, nearly.

"I have to say," said Jeremy, "that despite the success, I'm still not sold on biking. There are good moments, but it's mostly bad. And our machines were completely overshadowed by this incredible, beautiful, brilliant country."

"It's hard to sum it up," he concluded, as the sun dropped beyond the horizon and their eight days in Vietnam came to a peaceful, stunning close. "Perhaps that's why people, when they get back from this place, always say the same thing. **'Vietnam? You don't know man, you weren't there!'**"

AWESOME ADVENTURES:

Also Available:

ISBN: 978-1-40590-700-2